P9-APO-652

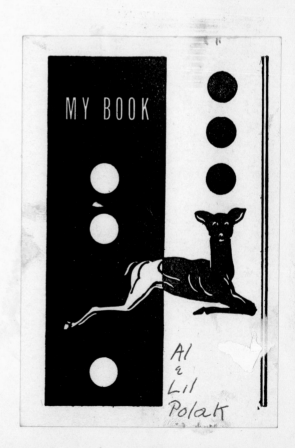

MY BOOK

Al
&
Lil
Polak

H. T. WEBSTER

THE BEST OF
H. T. WEBSTER

A Memorial Collection

With a Preface by

ROBERT E. SHERWOOD

and

A Biographical Sketch by

PHILO CALHOUN

Simon and Schuster • New York

1953

ALL RIGHTS RESERVED INCLUDING THE RIGHT OF REPRODUCTION
IN WHOLE OR IN PART IN ANY FORM
COPYRIGHT, 1914 TO 1953, INCLUSIVE, BY THE NEW YORK HERALD TRIBUNE, INC.
PUBLISHED BY SIMON AND SCHUSTER, INC.
ROCKEFELLER CENTER, 630 FIFTH AVENUE
NEW YORK 20, N. Y.

FIRST PRINTING

LIBRARY OF CONGRESS CATALOG CARD NUMBER 53-9691

MANUFACTURED IN THE UNITED STATES OF AMERICA
LITHOGRAPHED BY THE MURRAY PRINTING COMPANY, WAKEFIELD, MASS.

Table of Contents

Introduction

BY

ROBERT E. SHERWOOD

On April 4, 1953, the last new drawing by H. T. Webster was published in the New York HERALD TRIBUNE and a hundred and twenty-five other papers, and for many of us, millions and millions of us timid souls, this day was marked as one of life's darkest moments. There will be other fine artist-cartoonist-critics to inspire us with joy or indignation from day to day, but never another to span the years and the range of human emotions in the same extraordinary way that Webby did.

We therefore welcome this book containing some two hundred and fifty reminders of the fact that this tall, friendly, humble artist belongs in the highest traditions of American humor. He belongs with Ring Lardner, Will Rogers, George Ade, Finley Peter Dunne, Kin Hubbard, Heywood Broun, Montague Glass — yes, and with Mark Twain and Abe Lincoln.

It has often been assumed that the best of American humor came from the genial, homey, cracker-barrel school, as contrasted with the polished, rapier-tipped wit of the English, or the devious double-entendres of the French. Nothing could be more nonsensical. The distinguishing quality of our humor is its bite, its capacity to inflict wounds, to wield the meat axe or the whip. I remember that when Will Rogers met the death which he had so often courted—an airplane crash while pioneering new Arctic trails with Wiley Post —some pompous politician arose to pay tribute to Will, saying, "His humor was always kindly. He never said or wrote anything that hurt anyone."

Having known and loved Will Rogers, I am sure that if he thought this "eulogy" were true—if his frequent, bitter jibes at phonies, charlatans, stuffed shirts (including the very politician who uttered the libel) had failed to hit their targets and hurt them—he would be furious, he would feel that the best cracks of his career had been in vain.

Similarly, it would be deeply depressing to the admirers of H. T. Webster to learn that the members of the Ku Klux Klan dismissed his comments on this gruesome subject (an example appears on page 20) as merely harmless, good-natured spoofing.

One does not need to look to such violent examples as this one, or to the profoundly funny and pitiful commentary on the "liberation" of 1944 provided in the drawing called "Collaborationist" (page 111) to observe the iron that was in Webby's gentle soul. One may look to the snow-bound little dog and his frantic tracks (page 116) while his complacent masters are sunning themselves on a tropical beach, or to the superbly savage blast at "give-away" programs (page 213). There was probably not one of "The Unseen Audience" cartoons that did not offend or irritate somebody in the radio industry, nor can there be widespread disagreement that the victim in each case deserved to be offended and irritated, at the very least.

Webster denounced Wives, as a class, in "And There's Nothing You Can Do about It," and he excoriated Husbands, as a class, in "How To Torture Your Wife."

7

INTRODUCTION

In his admirable introduction to this book, Philo Calhoun (one of Webby's closest friends) points out that the artist's favorite target was himself, that his portraiture of the ineffable and immortal Caspar Milquetoast was sheer autobiography. That is unquestionably true, but Webby was also providing a revealing mirror for all the rest of us, with the exception of those unfortunates who live in a Hitleresque dream world of self-delusion and who fancy they are not impressed by signs that say "No Loitering."

In identifying himself with Mr. Milquetoast, Webby was aligning himself on the side of the Angels, he was standing up as one of the Pushed as opposed to the Pushers. He was our champion.

I first came to know Webby around about 1925 when I was Editor of Life (now always referred to as the old Life). We were putting together the big Christmas Number, and we thought it would be a great prize to have a contribution by H. T. Webster, who was attracting considerable attention with his cartoons in the New York World (this was the heyday of that memorable newspaper under Herbert Bayard Swope). Our Art Editor, Frank Casey, knew Webby and brought him to the office, but the artist was discouragingly diffident, he felt that his poor efforts could not compete in the fast company of a magazine that was published by Charles Dana Gibson; besides, he said, he didn't have an idea in his head. When he left, I was sure that we'd have nothing from him. But the next day he returned with a drawing which he unwrapped and offered, apologetically. He said, "Don't worry—if you don't like it, I can probably use it for the daily stuff." It showed a dismal newspaper office on Christmas. A haggard, jaded City Editor was giving an assignment to a callow reporter: "Go uptown and interview some of the poor devils who have to work and can't have dinner with their families today. Write a good sob story, about a column and a half. On your way back you might stop at a lunch wagon and get half a dozen hot dogs. Have 'em put on plenty of mustard. I won't be able to leave the shop all day."

I still have the reproduction we proudly made of that wonderful drawing.

Webby had a huge heart as well as a sharp bite. When you have known someone like him, you want to remember him and the contributions that he made to the art of living.

8

Biographical Sketch

BY

PHILO CALHOUN

Harold Tucker Webster was the name he got from his parents back in 1885 when he was born in Parkersburg, West Virginia. He always hated his first name, fought his way out of it in his teens, and has been "Webby" to his friends ever since. Coolish about even the last syllable of this harmless nickname, suspecting it might be a touch on the cute side, he always signed letters "Web," and drawings "Webster."

Webby had not yet reached his teens when the family moved to a small Wisconsin town which rejoiced (and still does) in the name of Tomahawk. George Ade said it was once on the map in pencil, but "some fresh drummer rubbed it out."

His father set up a drugstore there and Webby grew up rapidly into what O. O. McIntyre described as "an earnest, hard-working, gum-chewing freckled-faced boy." His school record was not distinguished. Even in drawing, he refused to hold his pencil as directed in Prang's Improved Drawing Course, spent his time making caricatures of the teacher, succeeded in getting the lowest mark in the class. Out of school hours he worked in the local brickyards, drove a grocery wagon, hustled freight at the railroad station, fished the neighborhood streams, read Mark Twain, drew endless sketches of everything and everybody.

A boy who worked in the harness shop at Tomahawk boasted that when he grew up he was going to sell horse collars set with diamonds to Mr. Vanderbilt. "An' Harold Webster is gonna draw little pictures."

"*Little* pictures!" retorted Harold; "I'm gonna draw *big* pictures! So big a million people can see 'em at once. I betcha million dollars I do!"

When Webby told the story many years later his cartoons were appearing in one hundred twenty-six dailies and his "Timid Soul" series in a score of Sunday papers, of a combined circulation of upwards of nearly twelve million copies. They were indeed "big enough" for a million people to see all at once. Said he: "If that boy really did sell those diamond horse collars, maybe I ought to collect."

At seventeen, Webby left Tomahawk for Chicago. He enrolled in Frank Holmes' School of Illustration. Twenty days later the school folded. This was all the art education Webster ever had except an earlier correspondence school course which he said he finished only because he had paid for it — in advance.

He drifted out to Denver, got some kind of a job with the *Republican,* quickly shifted to the *Post* when he was offered fifteen dollars a week as a sports-page cartoonist. "I knew it was more than I was worth," said he, "and was more than I could possibly spend, but I had to keep up the dignity of the profession." He held the job for two months and quit "just in time to avoid being fired."

Back to Chicago again, and some dreary weeks of job hunting before he landed a position with the Chicago *Daily News* where he worked for two years. His next move was to the Chicago *Inter-Ocean,* where his political cartoons began to attract attention. Before long they became a front-page feature and were apparently caustic enough to have inspired a bill in the state legislature prohibiting cartoonists from making pictures uncomplimentary to Senators and Representatives. It didn't pass, and the pictures continued.

It was during this period that Webby received what he always maintained was his greatest compliment. A man on an Elgin electric train went into convulsions (literally) over one of his cartoons about the Chicago School Board and was carried off the train to a hospital in a critical con-

9

dition. Someone asked Webby whether the convulsions were caused by laughter or wrath, and Webby replied that it didn't matter; it was the violence of the reaction which warmed his heart.

About 1908 Webby joined the art staff of the Cincinnati *Post,* where he stayed until 1911, when he started on his great adventure—a trip around the world. He was gone the better part of a year. Financially, the trip was a flop. Receipts from illustrated travel sketches did not even pay expenses. There were compensations of another sort, however, of which he became increasingly aware as the years passed. No one could take from him the memory of a trip up the Yangtse River in China with George Dorsey, author of *Why We Behave Like Human Beings,* then Curator of the Field Museum in Chicago. This adventure took the two young men nearly to the Tibet border, through a part of China in which no white man had ever been seen within the memory of the oldest inhabitant. At one point a flooded river nearly brought a quick end to Webby's career. Years afterward he could bring to life in a few sentences the horde of villagers standing on the river banks hopefully waiting for the foreign devils to drown.

Webby gained much from these months of the only real education he had ever known. He started out a boy and returned a man, mature in his thinking, adept in his art, broadened as only a highly sensitive personality can be broadened, by the impact of many cultures and many people.

Nothing less than New York would satisfy his growing ambitions at this point, and there he landed, almost down to his last hundred dollars, but fortified by a sturdy confidence in a talent which he knew was now worth a price.

For eight years he worked for a newspaper syndicate, doing political cartoons, and other drawings, including the series which he then called "Our Boyhood Thrills," and which delighted a later generation under the improved caption "The Thrill that Comes Once in a Life-Time." In 1915 George H. Doran Company published the first collection of his drawings in a book entitled "Our Boyhood Thrills and Other Cartoons."

One has only to look back forty years in the old files of America's foremost humorous journals to appreciate what crude and primitive fun-makers our grandfathers were. It was a commonplace to lampoon the Irish, the Jews and the Negroes in childish and cruel caricature. The mother-in-law joke was still going strong and the endless pranks of the Katzenjammer Kids were a Sunday dinner conversation piece. Webster's humor had a flattering subtlety, a robust geniality and a nostalgic warmth which appealed to many who were frankly bored with the slapstick pattern of the current funny men. Webby was bringing his art into higher levels of good taste, and nice people, who wouldn't allow an average, so-called "funny paper" in their homes, were laughing and remembering what they laughed at. Men began referring to him as "the Mark Twain of American cartoonists," and no accolade could have been more exact, or could have better pleased a man who knew *Tom Sawyer* and *Huckleberry Finn* almost by heart, and who all his life thought of Twain in terms little short of idolatry.

A boy barely out of his teens, Webby once drew a pen sketch of Mark Twain and sent it to him. Mr. Clemens' acknowledgment, to the effect that he thought the likeness "striking," was framed with his photograph and hung in a conspicuous place on the wall of Webster's living room to the day of his death. And it didn't spoil his pleasure a bit when the author wrote to a friend: "This morning I have received another heart-breaker. It comes from Webster of the Chicago *Inter-Ocean.* You will see yourself that it is too exact. This kind of accuracy, continued long enough, can ruin a man who is constructed as I am. I want to be pretty. I want to eliminate facts and fill up the gap with charm."

During the middle teens of the century, Webster had rooms in New York with R. N. Brickerhoff, cartoonist and illustrator, a product of Toledo, Ohio, and Ray Rohn, another artist of Ohio background. They called themselves "The Ohio Woman Haters' Club." Webby lost some caste with his fellow-members on one occasion when Lillian Russell rather publicly dubbed him "that Greek God, Webster," but was beginning to live it down when a young lady named Ethel Worts turned up in New York. Ethel hailed from Toledo and had come to town to study at Columbia and take some lessons in folk-dancing. Her fellow-townsman Brickerhoff persuaded his colleagues that the least they could do was to give her a cup of tea. Two weeks later, "after giving the matter profound thought," Webby drove her to the Little Church around the Corner, where they were married on August 2, 1916. There is a legend that part of the honeymoon was spent touring the country with Ringling Brothers' Circus — Ethel riding an elephant, and Webby doing a trick with the clowns. Anyway, they lived together peacefully and companionably for over thirty-six years.

During World War I Webby had charge of the cartoonists' section of the Division of Pictorial Publicity, which was a useful cog in the Liberty Bond sales organization. The favorite of his own drawings made for this cause showed a couple of eight-year-olds, one dressed in the height of fashion and guided by a proper governess, listening with solemn helplessness to the other, a ragged, grinning little gamin who gibes pridefully: "My Pa he bought a Libity bond he did." The caption: "The Beginnings of Caste."

In 1920, a drawing he made for the old *Life* showed a silly-looking Republican elephant in a nightgown kneeling beside a trundlebed. It was entitled: "If I should die before I wake," and was published shortly before the convention which nominated Warren G. Harding. It caught the eye of that old Democratic war-horse, William J. Bryan, who used it as the text for a political article. Webby referred to it as Bryan's "sermon." He didn't like it and felt that the cartoon must have misfired somewhere. He didn't like Bryan, either.

In 1919, Webster commenced his long association with the New York *Herald Tribune*. Except for a seven-year stretch with the New York *World*, which ended shortly before it suspended publication in 1931, Webster worked for the "Trib" and its syndicate for the rest of his life.

In this period he abandoned political cartooning almost entirely and was producing a succession of series drawings, each centered around some basic theme and pointed up by a catchy group title. Most of them lasted for years; at least three of them lived on for a generation or more. Death or suspended animation was due only to malnutrition. I can't think of any which succumbed to the deadly virus of a listless public.

"The Thrill That Comes Once in a Lifetime" and "Life's Darkest Moment," originally appearing under other captions, were the earliest of these and had the longest continuous run. "Poker Portraits" was always popular, but trailed off in the twenties, when Webby gave up poker for bridge. "They Don't Speak Our Language" and "Our Boyhood Ambitions" were almost automatically short-lived, because occupations which develop a specialized slang are not unlimited, and neither are the dreams of potentially famous adolescents. "Events Leading Up to the Tragedy," "The Beginnings of a Beautiful Friendship," "The Boy Who Made Good," "The Man in the Brown Derby," "And Nothing Can Be Done About It," and "Are You Listening?" were each a vital part of American life at intervals in the three decades following World War I. "How To Torture Your Husband (or Wife)" and "Trailer Tintypes" were late products. The last of all was "The Unseen Audience," hilarious satire on radio and television, which won him the Peabody Award in 1948, for distinguished service to radio.

Your dyed-in-the-wool Webster fan, like a Sherlock Holmes addict, or like me, is hard to persuade that any part of this tremendously versatile product is less workmanlike or indeed less amusing than any other. Each drawing is better than the last, and in the mass they have acquired an almost canonical sanctity in which priorities and preferments are scarcely to be recognized, except possibly in the two famous Lincoln's Birthday cartoons of 1918 and 1940. If your individuality must assert itself to the point of playing other favorites, then you had better cast a vote for the meek little man whom Webby created and named, and in whose person he poked endless fun at no less than H. T. Webster himself. Not that they looked alike. Webby was well over six feet tall and big in proportion, with a pink face, a lot of unruly white hair, a quiet, deep voice and a perfectly respectable chin. However, like Caspar, he had a profound respect for authority, and that included traffic signs, Canadian guides, investment counsel, weather reports, gas station attendants, peppery old ladies and income tax agents. I'm quite sure he was not lacking in physical courage, but he combined an almost hypersensitive consideration for the other fellow's feelings with an inherent distaste for rows, and there resulted a cautious approach to many normal situations, an almost naïve confidence in People Who Knew What They Were Talking About, which reached its ultimate joyous absurdity in Caspar Milquetoast.

Mr. Milquetoast first appeared as the unnamed hero of a cartoon in the New York *World* in 1924. It was several weeks before a second drawing in the series saw the light, and another month or two later a third picture introduced the little gentleman for the first time by the name which was to become a household word all over the world. Seven years later, Simon and Schuster published a collection of these cartoons in book form, and Webby lived to see the word "milquetoast" listed and defined in a standard dictionary.

Many of Caspar's experiences closely paralleled incidents in the day-to-day life of his artistic progenitor. Caspar had trouble with his car, his pipe, his golf, his fishing and his opinionated friends. So did H. T. W. himself. Webby loved to drive, but couldn't change a tire. He was an inveterate pipe-smoker, but the pipe had to be of a certain shape and the tobacco was made up specially on a personal formula. For several years he was a member of the Artist's and Writer's Golf Association, an outfit which arranged fantastic winter excursions to remote tropical golf links, and Webby tried conscientiously to justify his connection with this lusty group by learning the game. I doubt if he ever broke 100, but he taught Caspar to play, too, in dozens of hilarious golfing pictures.

Mr. Milquetoast took up fishing about the same time Webby did, sometime in the late twenties. The Websters had moved to a spacious house near the shore at Stamford, Connecticut, and had adopted as their family physician Dr. D. A. Shambaugh, who had offices in a nearby town. This was the "Doc" in scores of fishing and bridge pictures, and it was he who introduced Webby to fly-fishing for Atlantic salmon. For years Webby would come

up from Florida about the middle of April, to be sure of being on time for the inevitable telegram from Jack Russell, who ran the camp, that the ice was breaking up on the Mirimachi.

Four was the required personnel on these trips, because Webby had succumbed in a big way to the fascination of the bridge game, and long evenings at the card table were an essential part of the fun. The foursome finally crystallized into Webby, "Doc," Judge Webb of Fairfield and myself. For years we played every Tuesday during the months Webby lived north, and the same crowd arranged a week or two at Webby's house in Palm Beach sometime in the winter.

But card games and fishing, much as he enjoyed them, were, after all, only recreational sidelines. His great pleasure in life was people, and he attracted them in droves. It was an unforgettable experience to be in any gathering with him and to see how, without self-assertion or effort, his corner gradually became the center of the room. Webby's voracious reading, his wide contacts and his instinctive good manners had combined to make him a person of stature and consequence, entirely apart from his particular talent.

I have never known anyone with so many friends. Modest almost to a fault, he had a healthy aversion to pushing or climbing or intruding, but invitations to everything from neighborhood luncheons to fishing parties in Scotland seemed to pour in from everywhere. Wealth or position, race or creed, had no place in his own selective process. I have heard him talk politics and history with ambassadors and with gas-station attendants. It was just as much fun for him to swap fishing yarns with a Maine guide as with the editor of a nationally known sports journal. He played bridge with Charles Goren or with my youngest boy with the same zest and the same courtesy. Restraint and sincerity were the keys to his respect, and to even a moderate degree of intelligence and a flicker of humor he was generously responsive.

Webby never would make a speech in public and steadfastly refused to appear on television. He was heard on radio only once—a transcribed interview. For many years no one but his close friends knew of an acute arthritis which in 1927 cost him the use of his right hand. In three months he trained himself not only to write, but to draw, left-handed.

A few years ago the late Governor McConnaughy of Connecticut appointed him to the Governor's staff with the rank of Colonel. Webby was flattered and pleased at first, but became terrified when the Adjutant wrote, requesting measurements for a uniform. Webby never sent them. For two years he stayed in Florida an extra fortnight, until he was "sure the military season was over."

You wouldn't have to be with Webby very long to be conscious of how genuinely kind he was. You would probably never be told, for instance, that he never took a cent of the proceeds from the sale of original drawings (they all went to the *Herald Tribune* Fresh Air Fund), or that he financed some needy youngster for a college education. But you couldn't avoid being warmed by the succession of little thoughtful things which added up to as near a perfect score in human relations as it has been my privilege to see.

I remember on one of our fishing trips, a case of ale was stolen from our cabin. Someone else reported it, and the culprit, one of the guides, was caught and fired. Webby heard that he was the sole support of his mother. Nothing would do but he must hunt up the old lady, tell her he was sorry it happened, and give her enough to tide her over until the boy got another job.

I wish there were space to speak of particular drawings which will live as long as American home life retains its inimitable pattern. Most of them are included in this collection. Only when Abraham Lincoln and Tom Sawyer become dated, only when little boys no longer love little dogs, and men and women have no time or inclination to sometimes laugh at themselves, will H. T. Webster have lost the power to brighten our days and warm our hearts.

Webby died last fall, in a way which he might have chosen himself, had the choice been his. It was sudden, at the end of a happy week end with his old friends. It was at a time when age had not dimmed his view of life or his talent for expressing it. He would have sought no sounding epitaph, but I think he might have been content with what a great critic once said about Joseph Addison: "His tone is never that of a clown or of a cynic. It is that of a gentleman, in whom the quickest sense of the ridiculous is constantly tempered by good nature and good breeding."

I

Three Caricatures of H.T.W.

Drawn at various times by himself.

(Copyright, 1915, by H. T. Webster.)

TRYING TO THINK OF SOMETHING
FUNNY ABOUT POKER WHEN YOU'VE
BEEN HOOKED FOR $150 THE NIGHT
BEFORE ——
Copyright Press Publishing Co. (New York World) 1927.

II

Early Political Cartoons

Webster began political cartooning for the Chicago *Inter-Ocean* about 1908, but did little of it after 1919 when he joined the *Herald Tribune* Staff. He was normally a Republican; left the fold once, and temporarily, because of a personal liking for Al Smith.

GETTING ACQUAINTED WITH THE NEW BABY

"SOUVENIR, KIDDIES"

©1946·N.Y.TRIBUNE INC.

(Copyright, 1918, by H. T. Webster.)

ANOTHER STRAY PUP

ALL OF US WAR GARDENERS KNOW HOW YOU FEEL, WILHELM

THE PROHIBITIONIST FINDS A HORRID OLD DANDELION ON THIS ESTATE AND
WALKS HALF A MILE TO BURN IT IN THE KITCHEN STOVE

III

The Thrill That Comes Once in a Lifetime

and

Life's Darkest Moment

These two series had the longest continuous runs of all the Webster cartoons. Both titles were first used in the New York *Globe* about 1911. In the early days they were purely "kid pictures"; one started as "Our Boyhood Thrills" and the other developed from "Little Tragedies of Childhood," which dated from Webster's Cincinnati *Post* days. A collection of them (his first book) was published by The George H. Doran Company in 1915. Later both series included many other subjects; both are still going strong, months after Webster's death.

THE THRILL THAT COMES ONCE IN A LIFETIME

THE BOY WHO SHOPPED AND
SHOPPED AND EVENTUALLY
FOUND THE PERFECT CHRISTMAS
PRESENT FOR HIS MOTHER

Copyright, 1948, New York Herald Tribune Inc.

12-18-

THE THRILL THAT COMES ONCE IN A LIFETIME

THE THRILL THAT COMES ONCE IN A LIFETIME

THE THRILL THAT COMES ONCE IN A LIFETIME

THE THRILL THAT COMES ONCE IN A LIFETIME

THE ONLY WOMAN
IN THE WORLD CROSSES
AGAINST TRAFFIC

© 1938, N.Y. TRIBUNE, INC.

THE THRILL THAT COMES ONCE IN A LIFETIME

THE BOY WHO TOOK ALL HIS TOYS TO BED WITH HIM —

© 1937. N.Y. TRIBUNE, INC.

LOVE AT FIRST SIGHT

© 1937 N.Y. TRIBUNE, INC.

THE KIND OF LUXURY THAT
BRINGS ON REVOLUTIONS—
A HOMEMADE BARREL STAVE
HAMMOCK—

CAMOUFLAGE

THE BEST OF ALL POSSIBLE WORLDS

ONE OF THOSE NEW AND POWERFUL BICYCLE
LAMPS WITH SIDE LIGHTS OF GREEN AND RED,
NEW TOE CLIPS, NEW TURTLE NECK SWEATER
AND OYSTERS FOR SUPPER —

© 1939 · N·Y·TRIBUNE INC.

PROOF THAT THE FIRST MUSTACHE IS VISIBLE AT A DISTANCE OF ONE FOOT

THE THRILL THAT COMES ONCE IN A LIFETIME

(Copyright, 1916, by H. T. Webster.)

JESSE JAMES, ON HEARING THE PASSWORD, PULLS THE SECRET LATCH AND ADMITS COLE YOUNGER, THE DALTON BROTHERS AND BILLY THE KID TO THE BANDITS' LAIR —

© 1933 N.Y. TRIBUNE. INC.

THE THRILL THAT COMES ONCE IN A LIFETIME

THE THRILL THAT COMES ONCE IN A LIFETIME

THE THRILL THAT COMES ONCE IN A LIFETIME

OUT OF THE CHRYSALIS

©1940·N·Y·TRIBUNE INC.

THE AWAKENING TO THE VALUE
OF PUBLICITY AND THE SELECTION
OF A MEDIUM ASSURING A
TREMENDOUS CIRCULATION

THE THRILL THAT COMES ONCE IN A LIFETIME

THE THRILL THAT COMES ONCE IN A LIFETIME

THE CLINGING VINE

© 1933 N.Y. TRIBUNE, INC.

THE THRILL THAT COMES ONCE IN A LIFETIME

THE THRILL THAT COMES ONCE IN A LIFETIME

THE THRILL THAT COMES ONCE IN A LIFETIME

THE THRILL THAT COMES ONCE IN A LIFETIME

THE THRILL THAT COMES ONCE IN A LIFETIME

LEADING A SHETLAND
PONY IN A CIRCUS PARADE

(Copyright, 1916, by H. T. Webster.)

THE THRILL THAT COMES ONCE IN A LIFETIME

NO SNOW — NO ICE — NO SKATING —
NO SLIDING — TOO EARLY FOR
FISHING — TOO LATE FOR RABBIT HUNTING —
TOO WARM TO KEEP ON FLANNELS — TOO
COLD TO TAKE THEM OFF — TOO COLD
TO GO SWIMMING OR BAREFOOT —
EVERYTHING WRONG.

© 1938. N.Y. TRIBUNE. INC.

WILD FLOWERS
FOR MOTHER'S
BIRTHDAY

THE BOY WHO WAS
MAKING A SHIP MODEL

The Ureka Button Hook Company wishes one and all a Merry Christmas and a Happy and Prosperous New Year

FORM 9763
SERIES K

U.S. MAIL

U.S. MAIL

THE POSTMAN READS ONE OF THE 10,000 CHRISTMAS CARDS MAILED BY A FIRM TO ITS CUSTOMERS

Copyright Press Publishing Co. (New York World) 1928.

LIFE'S DARKEST MOMENT

Copyright, 1948, New York Herald Tribune Inc.

A BOY NAMED WILLIE SMITH ATTEMPTS A "CHRISTIANIA TURN" AND MAKES THE USUAL WILLIE SMITH TURN

© 1938. N.Y. TRIBUNE. INC.

"NOW FOR AN IDEA THAT WILL MAKE THE NATION ROCK WITH LAUGHTER"

THE GIRL, WHO FOR TWO WEEKS HAS USED ALL THE CREAMS, LOTIONS, SOAPS AND POWDERS RECOMMENDED BY THE HOLLYWOOD STARS, CONCLUDES THAT SHE IS NO MORE GLAMOROUS THAN USUAL ———

© 1941 - N.Y. TRIBUNE INC.

LIFE'S DARKEST MOMENT

THE DEATH OF SHERLOCK HOLMES

EEBSTER

Copyright, 1921, H. T. Webster.

THE ADMIRAL
WALKS THROUGH
THE STATION

THE DUDE

Copyright Press Publishing Co. (New York World) 1927

THE WELL—MEANING OLD
COOT WHO SPILLED THE BEANS

IV

Our Boyhood Ambitions

and

The Boy Who Made Good

Two early groups of drawings. The first stopped because of obviously limited material (the "boyhood ambitions" were in each case authentic), and the other because there were not so many things which aroused the cynic in Webster. As he grew older he became gentler and funnier in dealing with human frailty.

ANDREW CARNEGIE
WANTED TO BE A
NEWSPAPER REPORTER

WHAT WAS YOURS?

(Copyright, 1915, by H. T. Webster.)

THE BOY WHO MADE GOOD

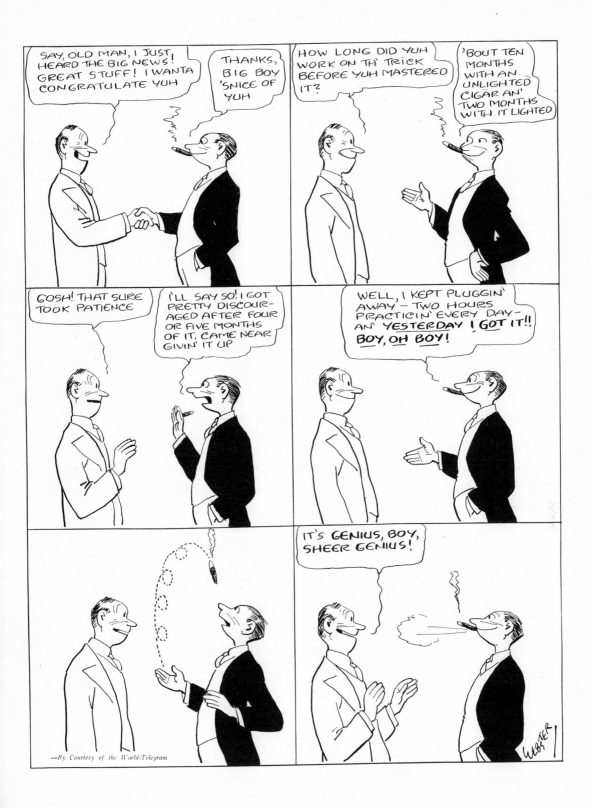

—By Courtesy of the World-Telegram

V

Dogs

There isn't a Webster series into which a few dogs didn't stray now and then. His latest book of cartoons *(Life with Rover:* 1949) collected the best of them. Mrs. Webster owned the poodles, but Webby liked them, too.

The most famous of these dog drawings was the one entitled "Collaborationist," a term in common use during the Second World War to describe the sort of Frenchman who played along with the Vichy (German controlled) government.

COLLABORATIONIST

© 1944 - N.Y. TRIBUNE INC.

THE COMMONER
WHO FELL FOR A
PRINCESS

HIGH STEPS

(Copyright, 1917, by H. T. Webster.)

"BUT FOR THE GRACE OF GOD THERE GOES FIFI"

VI

Poker Portraits

and

Bridge

The first group was one of Webster's most popular during the late teens and early twenties. It stopped when he gave up poker for bridge around the time of the big depression. He said no card game could survive "dealer's choice," "deuces wild," ten-cent limit and women players. A nostalgic pictorial record of the sturdy all-male jackpot game, with table stakes, was published in 1926 with a foreword by George Ade.

The first of his three collections of bridge drawings had come out two years before the poker book, and much of his best and funniest later work was done under the caption "Bridge."

THE PSYCHOLOGICAL EFFECT OF A BIG STACK

HOW OUR MOTHER USED TO PICTURE A FRIENDLY GAME OF PENNY
ANTE

THE FLOW OF WISDOM

THE BIG WINNER

THE INSCRUTABLE POKER FACE

THE WINNER OF A
BRIDGE TOURNAMENT
AND THE MAN WHO SAVED
EIGHTEEN PEOPLE FROM
DROWNING SHOW EACH
OTHER THEIR TROPHIES

© 1934 N.Y. TRIBUNE. INC.

THE COMEDIAN

ELECTION YEAR

THE CHATTERBOX

© 1938 - N.Y. TRIBUNE INC.

BRIDGE

© 1941 - N.Y. Tribune Inc.

BRIDGE

THE FIVE-HANDED GAME

© 1938 · N.Y. TRIBUNE INC ·

BRIDGE

TRYING TO MAKE A
FOURTH OUT OF AN
INDIAN GUIDE

PICTURE OF TWO MEN
LEAVING A BRIDGE GAME

© 1934 N.Y. TRIBUNE, INC.

VII

The Timid Soul

Webster is perhaps best known as the creator of Caspar Milquetoast, the Timid Soul, who first saw the light in the New York *World* in 1924. He has since appeared in books, movies, radio and vaudeville. In this series the artist literally added a word to the English language. "Milquetoast," with a small *m,* may be found in most modern American dictionaries.

MR. MILQUETOAST NEVER
LIKES TO BE SEEN LOOKING
AT UNDRAPED STATUARY

© 1940 · N.Y. TRIBUNE INC.

MR. MILQUETOAST KNOWS BETTER THAN TO TALK TO STRANGERS ON VITAL TOPICS

©1936 - N-Y-TRIBUNE INC.

MR. MILQUETOAST CONSENTS TO
POSE FOR A PHOTO TO BE USED IN
AN AIRLINER AD.
NOTE — THE PLANE IS ON THE GROUND

165

ON THE WAY TO THE OFFICE HE SUBSTITUTES HIS FRAYED OLD NECKTIE FOR ONE THE MISSUS GAVE HIM FOR CHRISTMAS

MR. MILQUETOAST DOES SOME QUICK THINKING

MR. MILQUETOAST SHIFTS
FROM FIRST TO HIGH

© 1936 N.Y. TRIBUNE, INC.

MR. MILQUETOAST DECIDES
TO TRY CHEWING TOBACCO
FOR THE FIRST TIME

© 1939 - N·Y· TRIBUNE INC.

Copyright Press Publishing Co. (New York World) 1930.

MR. MILQUETOAST DRIVES
OVER A TWENTY-FOOT
WATER HAZARD

THE LITTLE BOY NEXT
DOOR HAS BEEN PRACTICING
THE STAR SPANGLED BANNER
FOR THE LAST TWO HOURS

© 1941 · N.Y. TRIBUNE INC.

VIII

How to Torture Your Wife

and

How to Torture Your Husband

The artist himself has described this group as depicting incidents in the life of every happy family. He adds that the more the family can laugh at them, the happier it will be.

HOW TO TORTURE YOUR WIFE

THE ANGLER'S
BRIDE —

Copyright, 1948, N. Y. Herald Tribune Inc.

Copyright, 1948, New York Herald Tribune Inc.

© 1937. N.Y.TRIBUNE, INC.

WITH HIS EYES FULL OF SOAP HE GETS HIS INSTRUCTIONS

IX

The Unseen Audience

This is the series which at first caused an uproar in the radio industry, but in 1948 resulted in the Peabody Award to Webster "for distinguished service to radio."

PRELIMINARIES TO
ASKING IF WATER FLOWS
UPHILL OR DOWN HILL

Copyright, 1949,
New York Herald Tribune Inc.

BRIEFING THE
CONTESTANT

Copyright, 1948, New York Herald Tribune Inc.

225

Copyright, 1948. New York Herald Tribune Inc. 9-29

X

Fishing

There was never a series thus entitled, but, like dogs, fishing was the subject of many of the artist's best drawings. The collection published under the title *To Hell with Fishing* (1945) was by all odds the most popular of Webster's cartoon books.

For years at least one and often two or three fishing pictures appeared in the *Timid Soul* series toward the end of April, about the time Webby usually spent a week or two casting for Atlantic salmon.

DAYLIGHT
AHEAD

THE BEST FLY-
FISHERMAN
IN THE STATE

THE HONEYMOON

©1940·N·Y·TRIBUNE INC.

RESULT OF SIX HOURS OF FISHING

XI

Miscellany

TRAILER TINTYPES

THE SPOIL SPORT

LIFE'S DARKEST MOMENT

AND NOTHING CAN BE DONE ABOUT IT

ARE YOU LISTENING?

247

TRAILER TINTYPES

LIFE'S DARKEST MOMENT

BREAKING THE GOOD NEWS TO ANXIOUS PARENTS

LIFE'S DARKEST MOMENT

IF GEORGE HAD LIVED IN HOLLYWOOD

XII

Lincoln's Birthday

Webster's most widely known drawings were probably the two which follow. Lincoln was one of the artist's personal heroes, and when the series scheduled for publication on February 12 was appropriate, it was often the medium for a birthday tribute. Of the examples published here, the first appeared in 1919 and the other in 1941.

HARDIN COUNTY — 1809

ILL FED - ILL CLAD - ILL HOUSED

©1940·N·Y·TRIBUNE INC.

Bibliography

OF H. T. WEBSTER'S CARTOONS IN BOOK FORM

OUR BOYHOOD THRILLS AND OTHER CARTOONS, New York, George H. Doran Co., 1915

BOYS AND FOLKS, New York, George H. Doran Co., 1917

WEBSTER'S BRIDGE, *with William Johnston,* New York, Frederick A. Stokes Co., 1924

WEBSTER'S POKER BOOK, *with George F. Worts, Marc Connelly and R. F. Foster; foreword by George Ade,* New York, Simon and Schuster, 1926

THE TIMID SOUL, *introduction by Ring Lardner,* New York, Simon and Schuster, 1931

THE CULBERTSON-WEBSTER CONTRACT SYSTEM, *with Ely Culbertson,* New York, Frederick A. Stokes Co., 1932

WEBSTER UNABRIDGED, *introduction by Frank Sullivan,* New York, Robert M. McBride and Co., 1945

TO HELL WITH FISHING, *with Ed Zern; foreword by Corey Ford,* New York, Appleton-Century-Crofts, Inc., 1945

WHO DEALT THIS MESS, *with Philo Calhoun; foreword by Charles H. Goren,* Garden City, Doubleday and Co., Inc., 1948

HOW TO TORTURE YOUR HUSBAND, *with Caswell Adams,* Philadelphia, The John C. Winston Co., 1948

HOW TO TORTURE YOUR WIFE, *with Caswell Adams,* Philadelphia, The John C. Winston Co., 1948

LIFE WITH ROVER, *with Philo Calhoun,* New York, Appleton-Century-Crofts, Inc., 1949